PERIOD.

The Answers to the Questions You Didn't Ask

Shayla Gray-Parker

Illustrated by Shaquita Hughes

Published by TJS Publishing House
www.tjspublishinghouse.com
IG: @ tjspublishinghouse
FB: @ tjspublishinghouse

Cover design by Shayla Gray-Parker

Illustrated by Shaquita Hughes

Published in the United States of America
PAPERBACK ISBN: 1-952833-10-8
PAPERBACK ISBN-13: 978-1-952833-10-6

DEDICATION

This book is dedicated to you, the reader and supporters of the readers.
It is my hope that in this you find the answers to the questions you didn't know to ask.
Thank you for entrusting me to guide you through the journey to womanhood.

ACKNOWLEDGMENTS

Thank you God, for never allowing me to become comfortable with settling. To my family, thank you for showing me selfless sacrifice. For reminding me that the picture is always bigger than I however, without I, the picture is incomplete. To my friends, thank you for reminding me to never give up. To keep pushing forward, for your time, listening ear and countless bottles of wine. To my publicist and publishing company, it has been an honor and pleasure to conduct business with you as I charter these unknown waters.

INTRODUCTION

As a human being, I was skeptical in writing this book because I didn't want to fail. As a child of God, I knew I must be obedient. Often, as parents, we are unsure of how to begin the conversation of puberty with our children. Yet alone at what age to start the conversation and what words do we use? It becomes an awkward and uncomfortable situation for all parties. As children, we are dreading the day we must have "the talk" with our parents. I mean, we have already had parts of "the talk" with our friends, so we know it all already.

Yet, as a healthcare professional, I am the voice of reason. I hear the unspoken silence. I see the scared faces. I sense the confusion and tension in the air. I am the presence when no one is near. The hand that tucks in the bedsheets. The hand that comforts and the smile that says, "everything is going to be ok". I am the listening ear and am here to close the gap of the unspoken and bring back the power to where it belongs, to women.

Equipped with the tips in this book, "the talk" will become that much easier and the effects, long lasting. My prayer is that this book provides you with the tools needed to see the light at the end of the tunnel and the will to make it a memorable journey. May you find all the answers to the questions you didn't ask. Period.

A special thanks to Shaquita Hughes for the beautiful artwork, to all of those who have donated their time, stories and support. And to you the reader, thank you. Now, let's do this.

Disclaimer: The thoughts, words and opinions expressed in this book are solely my own. Implementing these options are done at your own risk. When in doubt, contact a healthcare professional.

1

GROWING UP GIRL
THE X CHROMOSOME

As you reach child bearing years (teenage years) your body begins to make the necessary preparations to conceive a child aka puberty. Your breasts begin to develop, your hips will spread, your skin changes and you start "smelling yourself" as your parents call it. Honestly, it's just teenage mood swings because your hormones are all over the place. More importantly, your uterus will begin to form a lining each month in preparation for impregnation aka pregnancy. And, each month that you are pregnancy free, your lining will shed through a process I like to refer to as "mini contractions" or menstruation.

Throughout your menstruation journey, you will experience stomach cramps, back pain and muscle pain which can result in an overall feeling of fatigue. This can begin a couple of days before your cycle begins and can last to the very last day. The good news is that the average menstruation cycle lasts about three to five days. During this time, you may feel like your life is over and you can't do anything you use to. You will cry over the slightest things, become irritable and angry towards people you care about or even become depressed. All the emotions you will experience during this time are normal and will pass.

Keep in mind, not only will you get through this, you will live through this and you WILL conquer this. Here are a few tips as to how.

"Mini contractions" or cramping can vary in intensity, duration and location. Invest in a good heating pad and over the counter pain medications such as Ibuprofen, Tylenol, Midol, etc. to combat these challenges.

2

Must Haves

These are items that you should invest in:

Essentials

- Pads, tampons, menstrual cups

- FLUSHABLE wipes

- Pain medication

- Heating pad

- Waterproof mattress pad

- Trashcan with lid

- Proper fitting underwear

- Baby Powder

A positive attitude also helps. Remember, you CAN and WILL do this.

Most females will wear sanitary napkins, pads, during their lifetime. Thankfully, the evolution of these items has changed a great deal since your mother and grandmother's time. They have been made to be thinner, more absorbent, more discrete and are no longer one size fits all.

There are many different brands: Kotex, Stayfree, Always, Playtex, L. Organix, are several of the more popular ones. Whichever brand you choose is up to you, however, I suggest one with wings. Wings on a pad help hold the pad in place, and catch any accidental side leaks. Keep in mind, you will need two different sizes, one size for your day to day life and one overnight size for a more controlled, restful night.

Invest in a waterproof mattress pad. Yes, I know you're a young lady and you don't wet the bed however, accidental leaks can make a mess of

your mattress. It is easier to clean blood from a thin, disposable or washable mattress pad then from your mattress itself.

If you choose, you can use a pad alternative during your cycle. There are several other options, such as tampons, menstrual cups and absorbable underwear, available at your discretion. These options are welcomed, but be prepared to become very familiar with yourself because some of these options are inserted vaginally. Make sure to read the contents of the packaging thoroughly to ensure that you are using them correctly.

If you choose an insertable device, wear a pad as a backup to control leaks as you become more familiar with your body.

Invest in a hand-held mirror. If you don't know what your vagina looks and feels like, then it's going to be that much harder to know when something is wrong.

Okay, it's now time to change your pad, but how? Go to the bathroom and clean yourself with regular toilet tissue? Not if you can help it. FLUSHABLE wipes are your new best friend. They provide for a better clean, reducing the left-over residue that toilet tissue leaves. Flushable wipes will also provide you with a sense of freshness and are septic system safe.

Your clean up should only require one to two flushable wipes for a normal clean and three to four flushable wipes for a combo clean. Combo cleans include a bowel movement.

Do NOT flush more than the recommended number of flushable wipes as your packaging recommends or else, you'll risk clogging the toilet. If you are in a public restroom and do not have flushable wipes, then there are other alternatives.

Dampen a paper towel and dab some soap on it. If you have sensitive skin, you can omit the soap as it can cause irritation. This works very similar to flushable wipes EXCEPT you DO NOT flush the paper towel. The paper towel goes into the trash can after use.

You've mastered the clean up! Now, what happens to the pad? This is where your small bathroom trashcan, preferably with a lid, comes into play.

Wrap your used pad in the new pads wrapper and place it into the trashcan. It's that easy!

By this time, you should have realized that blood has a distinct smell. By using a trashcan with a lid you can contain the smell, for the most part, decreasing the lingering odor that can otherwise be left in the air.

Scented trash bags work wonders at absorbing odors while releasing a fresh scent. Using this in combination with the lidded trashcan can save you from having to empty the trashcan as frequently.

Earlier, we discussed the need for an overnight pad, and there's a reason why. When it comes to sleeping, things can get tricky.

Thanks to our good friend gravity, what goes up must come down. The same goes for the direction of blood flow during your cycle.

If you lay on your stomach, blood will flow forward. Adjust your pad more to the front of your underwear instead of dead center.

If you lay on your back, blood will flow backwards. Adjust your pad more to the back of your underwear.

Side lying positions need no adjustments however, I do suggest bending the knee that is closer to the mattress to decrease the degree of the slant the blood will travel towards.

More importantly, proper fitting underwear is key! Although some of the women in your family may go for the worn, baggy, and less eye appealing underwear, usually called "period panties", these will not help you. Although boy shorts and thongs are cute, they will not help you either. Using a pad with the above listed underwear will leave your pad resembling folded origami. Regular fit briefs during this time is highly recommended.

To ensure a more proper fit throughout the day, you'll want to size down. If you typically wear a size medium, you will want to wear a size small. This will help your pad lay flat and decrease the risk of leakage.

As you'll be wearing underwear that are a size smaller than you normally would, be mindful of the increase of heat and sweat-- this can lead to skin irritation and chafing which is not uncommon during this time of month. Make sure your skin is dry during pad changes. Baby powder is a good way to dry the skin of any extra moisture. All you have to do is lightly powder the moist area. Got it? Great!

3

GETTING SCHOOLED

Always, always, *always* keep an emergency supply kit at school. At minimum, this kit should include:

- Three Sanitary Napkins

- Travel Size Flushable Wipes

- Once Extra Pair of Underwear

- Extra Bottom (pants, shorts, skirt)

Put these items in a separate carrying bag and leave it in your locker for those unexpected moments. ***This kit is separate from your usual monthly supplies. This kit should only be used in case of emergency and refilled accordingly.***

If you carry a small purse (crossbody, fanny pack, etc.) with you every day, it will be less noticeable for when you must go to the bathroom and handle business. No more sliding pads up your shirt sleeve hoping that no one notices.

The bell rings and it's now time to head to gym class. All you need to do to survive gym activities (running, jumping, etc) is to be honest. Yes, it's that simple. Generally, increasing your activity will temporarily increase your flow. Ask your teacher that you're having female issues, and that you need to be excused about five minutes earlier than the others. Remember to ask, not tell. This way, you'll have an adequate amount of time to clean up.

In gym class, you will sweat, and your underwear will become damp-- change them. Clean up with your flushable wipes, apply a clean pad or pad substitute and you're ready to go. However, if any portion of your extracurricular activities include being submerged in water (i.e. the pool), and you have not been acclimated to tampons or cups, STAY AWAY. Although your flow will slow in water, your pad will become fully engorged from the water-- this decreases its absorbency, leading to leakage and a hue that will form around you in the water. You've been warned.

More importantly, you can't spray perfume over funk! As much as we ladies love our perfumed scents, you need to be clean before applying if you expect a pleasant smell. Clean yourself first, then reapply a mist of spray as needed to refresh your scent.

4

HOME STRETCH

Now that you are home, feel free to bask in the greatness of a nice, warm shower. There is no such thing as being too clean, especially during this time of the month. If possible, I would recommend at least two showers per day and do your best to avoid excess heat throughout the day.

I understand some people may be concerned with over drying the skin and that is something I will take into consideration. On the other hand, I was active in school. I played sports and by the time someone tells you you need to wash, its too late. I also sweat in my sleep and there is no way sweat and menstrual fluid smell can produce a pleasant scent lol. That alone equates to washing in the morning before school and once home following extracurricular activities or even walking home on a hot Summer day.

Ask for a detachable shower head for your birthday, Christmas, or as a just because gift. The ability to guide the water right in the direction of your vagina will help remove the buildup from the day before.

It's now the end of your menstruation cycle. You've made it! Your period is finally over, and you are back to feeling like yourself. You can fit into your clothes again without the excess bloating, and you can leave home without your extra supplies. Let's celebrate! Treat yourself to a nice relaxing bath with your favorite bath bomb and body wash. While you luxuriate, let the water embrace you, play some nice music and sip on a cup of warm tea. You deserve it.

5

FAMILY TIES

As you embark on this journey, keep in mind that you are not alone. You are not the first female to begin womanhood, and you have to trust and believe that you will not be the last. Your mom, grandmother, aunts and any trusted female can be a great resource for you. They will understand you, even when you don't understand yourself and are too embarrassed to ask. So be nice to them.

Alternatively, your boyfriend, dad, grandad, and uncle have almost no clue. They can sympathize with you, and give you guidance from what they've learned from the females in their life, but they haven't experienced the physical and emotional strain that comes with menstruating. Most will do the best they can to help you, so take it easy on them.

With that being said, go to that sleepover, hang out with your friends and do everything you didn't think you could on your cycle. You are now equipped with the basic tools for survival.

Remember: One of the best things you can do for yourself is to take care of yourself!!

6

TIPS, TRICKS, & TECHNIQUES

- Birth control, in any form, can alter your cycle.

- Use cold water, not hot, to get out stains. Hot water will set the stain.

- Your skin may become oilier and/or drier. Drink water and stay hydrated.

- You will soil your underwear. Don't worry. Do wash immediately.

- Wearing dark bottoms for the first couple of days will make leakage spots less noticeable.

- Your menstrual cycle color will change from the beginning of your flow to the end. Dark red, bright red, and rust colors are all normal.

- Vaginal discharge can last a couple of days following the end of your cycle. Be prepared. Wear a panty liner.

- Tracking your cycle will give you a good estimate on when your next period will start. There are generally twenty-eight days in between cycles. There are apps on your phone that can help you track your flow.

- Wear a pad to bed the night before you are expected to start your cycle. This will prepare you in case you are asleep when it begins.

- Cycles are as individual as you are. Some are heavier, some are lighter. Some are shorter, some are longer. This is all normal.

- It's possible for you and your friends to sync cycles. This happens on a hormonal level and is beyond any level that I can explain.

- It is perfectly okay to spot clean, this means to take a wash up in between showers. Remember, if you can smell you, someone else can smell you.

- Once you get out of the shower, you have limited time before your flow restarts. Use this time to dry your private areas and put on underwear.

- Absorbable underwear is a newer option to use during menstruation.

- Sanitary pads are packaged individually and are clean, not sterile. Do not use it if the package is open.

- If you use a menstruation cup, the ideal place for adjusting it is in the shower. There you can take it out, empty and clean it in one location.

- If you empty a menstruation cup in the bathroom sink, clean the sink and counter with bathroom cleaner afterwards.

- If you are new to using tampons or insertable menstruation devices, try removing it every four hours. This helps you track your flow to determine how many hours you will be able to go in between changes as well as helps you learn the signs that you need to change your device. Lighter days will require less frequent changes whereas heavier days will require more frequent changes.

- The bathroom fan can help with the odor.

- Use your handheld mirror and examine yourself. Become familiar with how your body looks. If it doesn't look right, get it checked out.

- If you are sexually active, remember that you can get pregnant while you're menstruating.

- If you are sexually active, you can contract and/or transfer a sexually transmitted infection.

7
TESTIMONIALS

Hello beautiful young ladies, my name is Erica and I wanted to share a little insight as well as, encouragement about your period, or as I call her " Ms. Red." As we all know, when Ms. Red comes to town, she can be very annoying and can bring cramps and heavy bleeding along with her. As a young child, I remember Ms. Red visiting me when I was about 12 years old. I was a heavy bleeder at that age, and I use to wear the big overnight pads aka diapers. I remember bleeding so heavy, it soaked up my pad and came through my clothes. I know how embarrassing and what did I do? One philosophy that I lived by from then on out was to double up my pads, one in the front of my panties and one in the back. It was so uncomfortable, but I couldn't risk bleeding through all my cute clothes and being called out in school by my friends. This worked for me and at this time I was definitely not wearing a tampon. I encourage all of you to find out what works for you, if you have really bad cramps, use a heating pad or take some medicine for it. I say try to see the good in it. It used to make me laugh when friends would ask to do things and I would say no, or I couldn't do it because Ms. Red was in town. Furthermore, some of you may have longer cycles than others. My period lasted 3 days but I bled horribly. Some of you may have 5 days but may have no cramping or heavy bleeding. Periods are not as bad as you may hear, find out what works for you, always stay prepared and have enough supplies for accidents or slip ups. Periods are a part of life and makes you even more human, LOL. Always learn how to live, love, and laugh even when Ms. Red comes to town or other life situations; know that you are loved, and God bless you all."

~Erica J.

"*I started my cycle the summer of my 13th birthday. I woke up and my stomach was aching, and I just felt bad. It was a feeling I never had before. I went to the bathroom to pee as usual. This time when I sat down, I notice red blood inside my panties. I was so confused. I didn't get hurt so why was there blood? I called for my mom. When she came in, I showed her my panties and told her I had just took them off. She was like "What! What did you do?" I said "Nothing, I just took them off". She stood there for a few seconds repeating herself then she was like "Oh, oh, oh." She left and came back with a white square package. She gave it to me and said "put this in your underwear" and she walked out. No instructions, no directions, no explanation and oh, no clean panties. Thanks a lot. So, after getting some clean panties, I opened the package to find this extra-long, super thick pad (without wings). It was completely uncomfortable. I hated using these things. It limited all my athletic activities because the thing moved around all the time. Sometimes it was way up front and other times it was too far to the back. And let me tell you, adjusting a pad is hard to do in public. Hopefully, this won't be your experience, but if it is similar don't think your parent or caregiver doesn't care. Some people just aren't good with these types of things.*"

~ *Lynn G.*

"*Ah, mother nature. How it takes over our body at a young age! At that time, periods can be stressful, painful, but ultimately.... embarrassing! I remember when my period first arrived. I knew all about it. I knew how I was supposed to handle the situation, but when the time came, I was lost. I felt ashamed and embarrassed that his was happening to me. So, what did I do, tell my mom? No. I hid all evidence of a period. Taking messed up clothes and underwear and hiding them in places until I was able to sneak and wash them myself. This nonsense went on for months. Finally, my mother found my hiding spot. I was so scared. My mom didn't yell, she just asked why. Hmmm, why? Why did I do this? Why was this happening? I wasn't ready for this yet and I wanted to be normal. But after talking with my mom, I realized I was normal. Was I pleased with what was happening? No. I'm still not! (ha-ha). But I was content. As time passed, I became less embarrassed and more aware, more empowered, and more of a woman. The lesson? It is ok to feel a roller-coaster of emotions but know at the end of the day, YOU. ARE. NORMAL.*"

~*Nicole*

"The first time I saw blood it was a spot on back of friend's pants in 5th grade. I was so confused. Friends at school told me what was going on, but they were kids themselves, so you can imagine what that talk was like. I never got the actual "talk" from my mom. I remember sitting in the bathroom at home unsure what to do when I first saw blood in my own panties the following year. I called my mom to tell her. She asked through the door if I saw any pads in the closet. Still no "talk." We never used the word period in the household. I have heard her say monthly cycle a handful of times in my life. We typically never talk about it. As an adult, I still cringe until this day when women tell me about their periods or even say the word. When we finally had a "talk," a couple of years later, it was reduced to a 7-word summary: "Don't bring no babies in my house!" ☙ ⚲ The moral of this story: parents, talk to your kids. Educate them so that they won't be confused, ashamed of, or embarrassed by something so natural that can be a beautiful milestone in a young lady's life."

~ Shoni B.

ABOUT THE AUTHOR

Shayla Gray-Parker is a sister, daughter, wife and mother to two amazing bonus daughters. Since the young age of ten, caregiving for others has been a part of Shayla's life and she went on to earn a Master of Science in Nursing degree from Capella University and a Bachelor of Science in Nursing degree from North Carolina Agricultural and Technical State University (AGGIE PRIDE!). Currently practicing as a Registered Nurse in the healthcare field, Shayla uses her infectious personality, smile, and experience to capture and elevate the lives of others.

Made in the USA
Columbia, SC
10 December 2020